Acknowledgement

All copyrighted works in this collection are produced under license with print permission granted by the following publishers.

Acknowledged with special thanks to :

Faber Music Limited
Universal Edition (London) Ltd
Heugel Editeur, Paris
G Schirmers, Inc. – Music Sales Limited
Alfred Publishing Co. Inc.
Famous Music—Hal Leonard Corporation

The syllabus on which this anthology is based is
© **The Associated Board of the Royal Schools of Music**
Reproduced by permission of the copyright owner.

TEACHERS' CHOICE, SELECTED PIANO REPERTORY

(contains ABRSM examination pieces of the 2017 & 2018 syllabus)

Edited and annotated by Josephine Koh

CONTENTS

Grade 6

Pieces

Studies

CONTENTS

Grade 7

Pieces

Studies

Editor's Preface

This edition and compilation is drawn from authentic sources with suggested editorial for teaching and learning purposes. I would indeed recommend that teachers assist students to find for themselves the best approaches to meet an individual's musical needs - his sensibilities, imagination and technique.

Pedagogical suggestions are provided to help teachers make decisions on acceptable performance; such as articulation, pedaling and tempo. Editorials, as in performance practice, change with time. The approach in this collection would serve students needs for the current years and for taking ABRSM examinations. Performance perspectives concerning tone, sound, articulation, pedaling and dynamics may vary in different cultural and social situations. Teachers are thus encouraged to consult Urtext scores when in doubt or when this edition differs from their interpretative intents.

Fingering
They are suggestive and in no way to be conformed. Good fingering is important. Decide on what works best for a student based on:

    (i)   efficient facilitation of fingers that would help establish fluency in the playing.

    (ii)   the natural weight of each finger that would project a good sound and tone quality.

    (iii)   good, relaxed muscular control on the whole; over the hands, fingers and joints

Metronome markings
Most are suggested speeds to suit the mood and character of the pieces.

Articulation
Most baroque and classical works contain editorial suggestions which reflect the stylistic practices of the periods. These articulations, however, are often varied by performers.

Dynamics and performance directions
Additional editorial suggestions are indicated in brackets or below the scores.

Pedal Marks
Pedaling has been indicated in detail in most instances. Harmony plays a determinant role in making decisions on pedal changes. Special effects, stylistic features and other considerations based on the mood of a piece may require the use of the pedal in an unconventional manner. At higher grades, pedaling technique often becomes more demanding which often contribute to the overall effect of a piece. In most cases, a good musical performance requires good footwork and a sensitive ear to achieve the intended effects. Teachers may from time to time consider whether or not to use the pedal based on the period, mood and character of a piece.

Josephine Koh

Editorial Symbols

The following are explanations of editorial symbols used throughout the book.

Slurred notes, to be played *smoothly*.
They are usually found in original scores and sources.

Dotted slurs are editorial marks which suggest the notes are best played *smoothly in one musical direction.*

Long dotted lines indicate suggested *phrasing*, usually 2, 4 or 8 bars.

A mark used to indicate a *point of breath*, similar to a phrase.

The notes before is to be held to its *full value* but *separated* from the next. The effect is non-legato.

(3 1 2 4) An *alternative* set of fingering placed in brackets to facilitate fluency.

Pedal mark used to indicate the suggest downward and upward movement of the foot.

This suggests the use of *non-legato pedaling.*

This suggests the use of *legato pedaling* where the pedal change is made and depressed after the sounding of the next note.

The dynamic marking is editorial, i.e. not notated in the original sources.

Invention in A minor
BWV 784

♩ = 84

J.S Bach

J.S. Bach's collection of 2-part inventions is best known for its simple, yet highly effective contrapuntal writing. Based on the triadic motif of A minor, this invention presents imitative writing between the both hands. With merely quavers and semiquavers, the inversions, sequences and modulations create interest in the piece, best to be played with gradually varied and contrasting dynamics. The tempo mark, slurs, detached notes and dynamics are editorial. A consistent pulse has to be maintained, with clear finger articulation, evenness of the touch and prominence given to the melodic entries.

Rondo
3rd movt from Sonata in C, K. 545

Mozart

This ever popular sonata movement will be an appealing piece to most students. Written in the key of C major, the initial reading could be relatively simple. The main rondo theme is light-hearted, of which the skipping opening is soon followed by running semiquavers. Bars 9 -13, 38-41, 62-69 are technically challenging, of which the melody has to sound more prominent while the left hand accompanies. A metrical pulse has to be maintained almost throughout, with the possibility of slightly slowing down at suggested places. Good contrast and interest have to be maintained in the performance, of which most of the dynamics and slurs are editorial.

Blank Page

Andante

3rd movt from Pastorella in F, BWV 590

J.S. Bach

This movement taken from J.S. Bach's collection of organ works is a charming and beautiful piece. The walking pace in 3/8 time features a singing melody quietly accompanied by lightly pulsating chords. The C minor tonality gives the piece an innate quality with the melody gently rising and falling. Elegant ornaments – the grace notes, lower mordents and mordents, contribute to the mood of the Baroque pastoral setting. Tied notes create a sense of longing and suspense with the occasional short dotted rhythms breaking off any sense of monotony. All dynamics, slurs and phrase marks are editorial. For clarity of tone colour, the use of the pedal is to be avoided.

8

Blank Page

Andante
1st movt from Sonata in G minor, Op. 49 No. 1

Beethoven

It is rare for the 1st movement of a sonata to be rather slow. Nevertheless, this movement reveals Beethoven's expressiveness. The opening bars take on a chordal texture in G minor before homophony in B flat major takes over at bar 17. The mood livens up, with detached notes and decorative turns. The development beginning at bar 35 has an aggressive nature, with the trills on f. Soon the mood lightens from bar 40, with a series of high notes and quick demisemiquavers. The recapitulation occurs at bar 66, bringing back the original materials. The deep and quiet coda from bar 99 ends the movement on a low G major chord.

Sonata in F

Kp.378 (L 276)

Scarlatti

This Scarlatti sonata in F major has a bright and skipping opening motif. The 2 -part texture the with clear counterpoint makes this piece a delight to play. Varied articulations would provide much interest to the work and thus the suggested slurs, staccatos and dynamics. A contrasting, more lyrical moment is brought about with the shift to in the minor keys - F minor (bars 20-25) and C minor (bars 29-42) before closing the first section in C major.

The 2nd sections introduces D minor at bar 54. The character turns slightly dramatic.

The return to F minor at bars 76 -89 serves as an effective means for the piece to return to its tonic major.

Blank Page

Los Tres Golpes
(The Three Strikes)

Cervantes

Allegro ♩=96

marcato il canto

The character of this Romantic Cuban dance is immediately presented in the opening 4 bars. The melody, marked with accents, portrays a strong sense of passion within the quick 2/4 time. The texture thickens at bar 5, with syncopation and added inner parts. At bar 13 -16, G major brightens up with higher pitched double notes and further thickening of the chords. Bars 19-20 bring about the climax in the piece. The closing section is in the joyful key of E major, with quick rhythms from bars 25 till the end, a clear contrast from the initial key of E minor.

Andantino in A flat

No. 57 from *Klavierschule*

Hummel

The use of double 3rds and the chordal structures of bars 1 to 16 need good coordination and rhythmic accuracy in both hands. Nonetheless, once the initial stage of note reading and working with hands separate are overcome, this piece has much musical interesting. With short motives, regular phrases and varied rhythms, the quick changes of dynamics feature the 'sturm und drang' (storm and stress) elements of the early classical period.

The 2nd section, from bars 17 – 22 creates a sudden *ff* contrast with pulsating chords; yet from bar 22 -25, oscillating semiquavers in the right hands become an accompanying figure for the left hand. The material of the opening returns at bar 27. The challenging runs of this final section, from bars 31-37 are melodious. Kept at a consistent tempo with a firm metric pulse, this piece with its varied ideas and dynamics is possibly a joy to play.

Pohádka (Fairy Tale)

No. 4 from *Loutky (Puppets)*, Book 1

Martinů

A 'Fairy Tale' from the collection of piece 'Puppets', this pleasantly elegant piece by Bohuslav Martinů (Czech composer), emerges within the light and transparent harmonies. The bell-like effect of bars 8, 10, 25 and 27 are noteworthy - which requires a relaxed falling touch of the hand onto the 5th finger , soon to lean onto the thumb.

A magical section with strange harmonies and unusual grouping of notes in the Trio section at bar 33 breaks the calm mood and begins to create a swirling effect with the left hand quavers.

At bar 48, the register broadens, as the accompaniment reaches into the lower bass notes. The first moderato section is then repeated. The pedal markings and dynamics are provided in the original score, of which only fingering is editorial.

Modulations
from Blue Piano

Mike Cornick

This calm and relaxed jazz piece is ingeniously composed. The opening 4 bars present the crushed notes, with various chromaticism in the right hand and syncopated rhythms. The harmonies are captivating, of which a slight accent on the 1st and 3rd beats with a swing effect would work nicely with the rise, ebb and fall of the melodic lines. One can imagine a variety of instruments, of which the low range notes at bars 9-12 would sound like a saxophone. At bar 13, the melody moves to a higher register, as if a trumpet takes over. Much is to be enjoyed. The pedal marks are suggested to create an ambience that would support the overall effect of this 'blue' piano piece.

Moderate

1st movement from *Suite for Piano*

Dello Joio

Moderato ♩ = 92

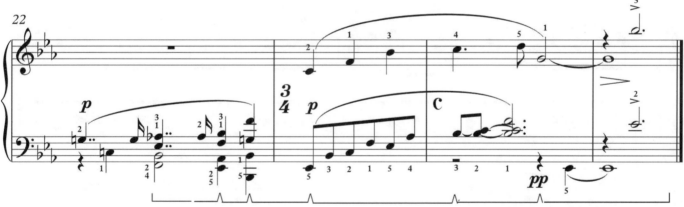

The piece reveals much use of 4ths – quartal harmonies at the opening. The melody enters at bar 5, with the left hand in counterpoint. The range of notes vary between both hands, moving into various registers with their unconventional harmonies. The tonal centre of E flat remains vague, with seemingly prominent recurrent musical shapes and rhythmic elements. The phrasing is defined by each group of smoothly flowing ideas. Despite the varied time signatures, this short piece comes across as calm and well constructed.

Decorative Appoggiaturas
Op. 599, No 81

Czerny

Right Hand in Syncopation
Op. 599, No. 85

Czerny

Allegro ♩= 126

Rhythmic Arpeggios
Op.849, No. 15

Czerny

Allegretto vivace ($\quad$ = 80)

Fugue in C
from BWV 953

J.S. Bach

This 3-voice fugue begins with a simple 2-bar subject, based on alternating notes that descends from C. The voices – Soprano, alto and bass enter in order of appearance and the fugue spins off from bar 9 to 12 in 2 parts. The 3-part contrapuntal texture returns at bar 13 and the subject is heard in the bass of bar 17. Almost all quavers should be played detached and the semiquavers, legato. The tempo is to be taken moderately quick. With a delicate touch and clear finger articulation, the baroque elements of this harpsichord piece would emerge.

Presto
3rd movt from Sonata No. 5 in F

This 18th century piece has a very lively and appealing character. The opening 2-bar broken chord motif followed by 6ths in the right hand immediately establish the first 8-bar phrase of the 1st Subject in F major. Even and agile fingerwork are important, without a heavy touch. The 2nd Subject begins at bar 13, with its lively flow of dotted notes and semiquavers. The runs may well be played with an elegant feel that would express the stream of musical flow and direction. Light staccatos are suggested for the alternating notes of the right hand in bars 37-39 and similar passages. The exposition ends at bar 48 in C major. In the typical tripartite sonata form, the development begins at bar 49. The recapitulation of the 1st subject is soon heard at bar 103, with the 2nd subject at bar 119.

Scottish Legend
Op. 54 No. 1

A. Beach

Lento con molto espressione ♩ = 63

(pedal similarly throughout the piece)

The tonality of D establishes a melancholic and modal quality which resonates in the melody in the highest part. As the titles suggest, this Scottish legend conveys a deep sense of nostalgia. The chordal texture creates an antiquated effect of which the opening rising chords seem to yearn, tapering off in the 2nd bar. Bar 3 recalls the idea at a 3rd higher, with bar 5 being at the loudest and most heart felt. Arpeggiated chords have to be spread out expressively - in a singing manner, rather than to be rolled out too quickly. Tempo rubato has to be employed, as led by the direction of the chords and melody - with a tendency of pushing forward with each phrase and pulling back at the end of it.

Blank Page

Nocturne

No. 8 from *Nocturnes*

Grade 7
B : 5

F. Poulenc

Très modéré ♩ = 72

Mettre beaucoup de pédale (le chant doucement en dehors, les batteries très discrètes)
To use much of the pedal (singing sweetly and distinctly, keeping the set of accompanying chords very quiet)

(continue to pedal similarly, changing with the harmonies)

This peaceful French piece has a serene quality. With a beautiful singing melody in the uppermost part, which should ring amidst the chordal texture. While it may not be technically very difficult, having to achieve a sustained melody with the 4th and 5th fingers and keeping the chords quiet can proof to be a challenging skill for the student. At the initial stage of learning, it would be helpful to practice the melody on its own, with the pedal. The pedal changes have to be performed smoothly, without causing any unnecessary bumps to the musical flow. While Poulenc has indicated the dynamics, it is often possible to include more nuances – the gradual crescendos and diminuendos that are musically intended, including the occasional rit. Such suggestions are indicated in brackets in the score. The pedal markings are also editorial.

No. 1 from Moments Musicaux,

Op. 94, D. 780

Schubert

Schubert's moments musicaux (musical moments) is a collection of lyrical and expressive piano works composed in the early romantic period. This 1st musical moment is in a minuet and trio form, with the minuet section in C major and the trio section in G major – as it rolls forward on seamless triplets from bar 30 to 66. This piece can be technically and musically challenging for the Grade 7 student – the series of staccato chords, slurred couplets, quick changes of rhythms, cross rhythms of 3 notes against 2, and playing **pp** for the low triplets in bars 38 – 50.

(pedal similarly)

While an almost strict and consistent pulse is kept, the romantic and expressive elements of Schubert's writing can be felt in the mysterious and low rumbling triplets of bars 59 to 66; before the return of the minuet section at bar 66 in C major.

francee?

Willie Wagglestick's Walkabout

No. 4 from *Jazzy piano 2*

Brian Bonsor
(1926-2011)

The boogie walkabout would be an attractive and enjoyable piece for most students. The rhythms may be difficult to catch on initially. But some separate hands practice with a metronome would help. The idea of the boogie jazz style is to acquire a touch that is not too legato, being more rhythmic instead. It is important to observe all off beat accents, though a consistent pulse is to be kept throughout, except towards the end. For the shakes at bars 24, 33 and 34, it would be effective to create graduations of crescendo and decrescendo within. Pedal marks are editorial.

Blank Page

Bright
2nd movement from *Suite for Piano*

Dello Joio

The opening may present jarring harmonies and awkward rhythms in the right hand with wide angular melodic leaps. For the left hand that could not span the 10th in bar 3, playing the D flat an octave higher, taken by the right hand may be a good solution. The exotic melody is introduced at bar 4. It is repeated with changing accompaniment parts.

As the intended effect is 'Bright', the touch is for the piece at *f* and *ff* would be strong and loud but not heavy. The pulse has to be kept constant throughout, of which dynamics and articulation have to be faithfully adhered to. It is an exciting piece to play, when all the details are observed and keyboard techniques achieved.

Ray's Blues

Dave Grusin

Moderate Blues tempo ♩. = 80

This piece is taken from the film score 'The Firm'. It portrays a melancholic mood, of which the blue scale and rhythms create an easy laid back effect. As with all jazz music, the quavers need not be played evenly, but the pulse has to be kept constant throughout. The harmonies are interesting, of which students would need time to study the notes and pay attention to all syncopations and tied notes. Improvisatory passages in the right hand, such as in bars 14, 20, 23-24 should sound rhythmic rather than all smooth. Much liberty in time can be taken for the final bars. The pedal has to be used; but care has to be taken to avoiding cluttering the notes or harmonies. All pedal marks are suggested and editorial.

CODA

Blank Page

Cross Hand Melodic Lines

Op. 849, No. 27

Independence of the Fingers

from *Gradus ad Parnassum, The Art of Piano Touch*

Clementi

Allegrissimo ♩ = 132

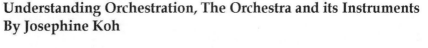

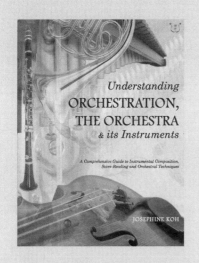

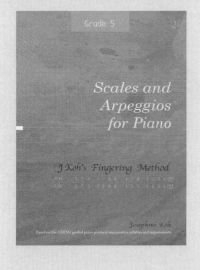

Understanding Orchestration, The Orchestra and its Instruments
By Josephine Koh

The study of orchestration is an integral part of every musician's education - the composer, conductor, performer, teacher or advanced student. Numerous treatises have been written on the subject and on instruments of the Western orchestra. Yet this volume takes on a practical comprehensive approach by presenting useful information essential for the effective mastery of score-reading and analytical skills. Structured in two parts, it introduces the world of instrumental sounds and gradually unravels the art of instrumentation in canonic works. This study text is suitable for music students and instrumentalists preparing for advanced graded and diploma examinations, music teachers, young composers and conductors who need relevant insights into score-reading and orchestral techniques.

Scales and Arpeggios for Piano (Grades 1 to 8)
J Koh's Fingering Method

Students can now learn scales and arpeggios in the most enjoyable and effective way. J Koh's *Fingering Method* develops the learners' technical skills by using a combination of visual, auditory and tactile systems. Now available in print, this proven method used for training gifted children is specially produced to assist students prepare for the ABRSM graded piano practical examinations. Success assured! The series from Grades 1 to 5 focuses on establishing good fingering habits. The *Fingering & Tonality Method* for Grades 6 to 8 continues the development of technical competence in piano students based on key and chord structures.

Practice in Music Theory (Revised Edition)
by Josephine Koh

The revised edition of the *Practice in Music Theory* Grades 6 to 8 is the continuation of a highly recommended series of instructional course books for students who wish to achieve a high standard of competence in harmony, counterpoint, melodic writing and score analysis. The J Koh's teaching approach is academic and logical, yet musically conceived. Based on the ABRSM syllabus, this Grade 6 course book is in 2 parts.

Part I— The principles of 4-part writing, concepts of harmonic progression, voice-leading and non-harmony notes are clearly presented, with progressive exercises.

Part II— Techniques of melodic writing and score analysis are developed, with terminologies explained; illustrated with examples.